-SAVE THE
ANIMALS

Published by Evans Brothers Limited
2A Portman Mansions Chiltern Street
London W1M 1LE

Cloverleaf is an imprint of Evans Brothers Limited

Cover design by Design Revolution, Brighton

First published 1990

Typeset by Fleetlines Typesetters Ltd., Southend-on-Sea
Printed in Hong Kong by Wing King Tong Co. Ltd

ISBN 0 237 51153 3

This book is dedicated to Florence Lewis

~SAVE THE~
ANIMALS

Wendy Lewis

Cloverleaf

An imprint of Evans Brothers Limited

Monday again! School again!

Everything seemed the same.

Some children arrived at school early. They played the same games, made the same jokes, saw the same faces. . .

The same faces?

What are those animal faces in the classroom window? They are not the same. They are new!

"Look!" said Jake. "We have some visitors. I wonder what's going on?"

"Yes," said Sally, looking over Jake's shoulder. "I don't want to sit next to that rhino, but the panda looks friendly. Come on, let's go in and see what's happening."

"Let me introduce you to some special animals from around the world," said the teacher. "They are special because there are not many of them left in the world today. They need new friends like you to help save them. Now, what can we do for them?"

"What about a circus to raise money?" suggested Sally.

"No, what about a **people** circus?" called out Jake.

A **people** circus to save the animals! Everyone thought that was a really good idea.

The teacher said they could begin organizing it right away.

First of all the children went into town to find the mayor.

Sally and Jake told him about the people circus.

"I've always wanted to help the giant pandas," said the mayor. "They eat a special kind of bamboo but people have cut down many of the bamboo forests. When your circus is ready, I will give you a big tent for the show."

Then the children asked Mr Green the grocer to help.

"Me? What can I do? I only know one trick. But if it will help the mountain gorillas, I will be in your circus."

"Why do you want to help the gorillas?" asked the children.

"Because people hunt them and cut down the forests where they live. There are only about 400 mountain gorillas left in the world now," said Mr Green.

The shop smelled good. It was full of cakes and cheese and sweets and fruit.

"What do gorillas eat?" asked Jake.

"Well, lowland gorillas eat fruit, and mountain gorillas eat the leaves of shrubs and vines," said Mr Green. "But if the forests are cut down they will have nothing left to eat."

Then Mr Green tried out his trick with oranges. Jake gave him two at a time to throw: first two, then four, then six, then **eight** oranges in the air at once!

"No more, Jake!" laughed Mr Green. "I shall drop them all. Well, am I good enough for your circus?"

"Of course! You can be the juggler," said the children.

The children decided to hold an exhibition in the local library.

They painted pictures and wrote stories about the animals in danger. Sally painted the giant panda, and Jake painted the mountain gorilla. Then they pinned all the pictures and stories on the walls for everyone to see.

The people in the town liked the exhibition. They found out about some of the animals that need help.

They saw pictures of pandas, gorillas, tigers and elephants. They saw pictures of rhinos and snow leopards.

Lots of people wanted to join the people circus.

Later, the children went to find more acts for their circus.

"I will be your clown," said Flap Jack, the baker. "I want to stop people hunting tigers and cutting down the forests where they live."

Mr Lock, the ironmonger, said he knew a few rope tricks. "I want to help the rhinos. They are killed for their horn."

Miss Tiptoe from the dance centre and Mr Chip from the china shop also wanted to help.

"I want to stop people killing elephants
for their ivory tusks," said Mr Steel, the roadworker.
"And we must protect the forests and grasslands where they live."

Mr Wafer, the ice-cream man, knew what he wanted to be
in the circus but said his idea was a secret.

The Wang family, who ran the Chinese restaurant, said
they wanted to be acrobats.

Mr Pane, the window cleaner, said he wanted to be
something high up.

"Now you have found all your performers, we must get ready for the show," said the teacher.

The children had a great time painting tins, boxes and banners – and their faces! Would they be ready on time?

The people in the town stopped to watch the fun.

"Where can we buy tickets for the show?" they asked.

The tickets were on sale in all the shops. Soon they were sold out – everyone wanted to see the show and help to save the animals.

But the show was still not ready. The children had more work to do.

On Wednesday, the children arrived at school early. They wanted to finish their work on the circus.

"Circus performers always dress up," said the teacher. "We shall need lots of material to make some costumes."

The children searched in cupboards and went to jumble sales. They collected old clothes, old curtains and table cloths.

They cut out trousers and tops. They sewed on buttons, and stuck on stars and spots. They tried things on and giggled a lot. They did look funny!

Then, through the window, Sally spotted some people. "Come on Jake! Let's see what's going on outside."

The circus performers were practising in the playground.

"I will play the music," said Curly, the hairdresser. "I want to help the snow leopard. It is hunted for its fur."

Mr Steel wanted to be the circus strong man. ''I am not as strong as the elephants,'' he said. ''But I am strong enough to help save them!''

Mr Lock also needed saving! He was tied up and toppling over. ''I hope my trick works at the show tomorrow,'' he said sadly.

At last it was time for the people circus!

Mr Wafer arrived early. He was the ringmaster. First he checked the tickets and then he welcomed everyone to the show.

There were grandmas and grandads, mums and dads, uncles and aunts and brothers and sisters. There were clowns and acrobats, jugglers and dancers. There were banners and balloons and streamers.

"This is the first time I have been to a **people** circus," said one person in the crowd.

"I am glad there are no animals," said another. "They are happy in their own lands, and this is such a good way to help them."

The people went into the tent to watch the show.

The show began. Mr Pane had the best view of all on his stilts. He and Jake tried to help Mr Green with his juggling.

Miss Tiptoe danced across the ring to the sound of Curly's flute, and Mr Chip only broke a few plates!

Flap Jack liked the paper stars that rained down from the Wangs' bucket. They did not make him wet!

Mr Lock, the escapologist, was still tied up. Would he escape by the end of the show?

Then Mr Wafer asked everyone to remember the Save the Animals fund.

Some of the children went round collecting money.

The people circus had been a great success!

A few days later the children invited the mayor to watch a video at school. The video was about the animals they wanted to help.

At the end they made a list of ways to help the animals, and this is what they wrote:

Ban hunting and poaching.
Protect rare animals in their own lands.
Ban the sale of ivory, fur and skins of rare animals.
Ban the sale of rare animals as pets.
Save the feeding grounds of rare animals.
Tell other people about the animals in danger and
ask them to help.

"Your circus money will help to do some of those things,"
said the mayor. "And here is something else that will help.
Our local newspaper has started a competition to find
more good ideas like Jake's people circus. This poster
tells you about the competition."

"I will ask all the shopkeepers to put a poster in their windows. You have done a wonderful job. I want to thank you all for helping to save the animals.

If the animals can stay free in their own lands, the world will be a much better place for them **and** for us."

Perhaps YOU can help to organize an event to help save the animals. They certainly need all the help you can give them.

All these animals are either endangered or threatened with extinction. Which of these animals can you find in the book? What do you know about them?

1	Musk Ox	16	Mouse-eared Bat	31	White Rhino
2	Polar Bear	17	Wild Cat	32	Malayan Tapir
3	White Whale	18	Asiatic Black Bear	33	Philippine Tapir
4	Kit Fox	19	Grey Wolf	34	Dugong
5	Big-Horn Sheep	20	Snow Leopard	35	Proboscis Monkey
6	Prairie Dog	21	Mandrille	36	Babiroussa
7	West Indian Manatee	22	Addax	37	African Elephant
8	Tassel-eared Squirrel	23	Monk Seal	38	Hump-backed Whale
9	Volcano Rabbit	24	Simian Jackal	39	Koala Bear
10	Two-toed Sloth	25	Markhor	40	Hippopotamus
11	Giant Anteater	26	Yak	41	Ring-tailed Lemur
12	Golden Lion Marmoset	27	Mountain Gorilla	42	Grey Kangaroo
13	Jaguar	28	Leopard	43	Leadbeater's Possum
14	Otter	29	Tiger	44	Rat Kangaroo
15	Pine Marten	30	Panda	45	Duck-billed Platypus